elf

Sheet Music Selections
from the Motion Picture

Contents

Produced by
Alfred Music
P.O. Box 10003
Van Nuys, CA 91410-0003
alfred.com

Printed in USA.

ISBN-10: 0-7390-9654-0
ISBN-13: 978-0-7390-9654-3

PENNIES FROM HEAVEN

Words by
JOHNNY BURKE

Music by
ARTHUR JOHNSTON

C
D9sus
D13
Dm7
G7
Dm9
G7
C
Trade them for a pack-age of sun-shine and flow - ers.
If you want the
l.h.
C7
C7(♯5)
F
Dm7
Fmaj7
Fm(maj7)
Fm7
things you love, you must have show - ers.
So when you hear it thun - der,
Em7
C9
B9
B♭9
A9
Dm
D7
G7
don't run un - der a tree.
There'll be pen-nies from heav - en for you and
1.
C
A♭7
G7
me.
2.
C
A♭7
C
me.

SLEIGH RIDE

Words by
MITCHELL PARISH

Music by
LEROY ANDERSON

Gmaj7
G6
Am7
D7
snow is fall - ing and friends are call - ing, "Yoo hoo." Come on, it's
love - ly weath - er for a sleigh ride to - geth - er with you. Gid - dy -
G
C
C♯m7
F♯7
B
F♯
yap, gid - dy - yap, gid - dy - yap, let's go, let's look at the show,
we're rid - ing in a won - der - land of snow. Gid - dy -

Bm7
E7
A
yap, gid-dy-yap, gid-dy-yap, it's grand, just hold-ing your hand.
Am7
D7
Am7/D
D7
We're glid-ing a-long with a song of a win-ter-y fair-y-land. Our cheeks are
Gmaj7
G6
Am7
D7
Gmaj7
G6
Am7
D7
nice and ros-y and com-fy co-zy are we. We're snug-gled
Gmaj7
G6
Am7
D7
G
B♭
D7
up to-geth-er like two birds of a feath-er would be. Let's take that

Gmaj7
G6
Am7
D7
road be - fore us and sing a cho - rus or two.
Come on, it's
love - ly weath - er for a sleigh ride to - geth - er with you.
1.
G
C
To Interlude
There's a
2.
Fine
you.
dim.
p
f
Interlude:
birth - day par - ty at the home of Farm - er Gray, it - 'll

G6
be the per - fect end - ing of a per - fect day. We'll be
G♯dim7 Am7 A♯dim7 G/B B7 Em C♯m7(♭5)
sing - ing the songs we love to sing with - out a sin - gle stop, at the
legato
B/F♯ C♯m7(♭5) C♯m7 F♯7 B G♯dim7 D7
fire - place while we watch the chest - nuts pop. Pop! Pop! Pop! There's a
Gmaj7
hap - py feel - ing noth - ing in the world can buy, when they

pass a - round the cof - fee and the pump - kin
G6
G♯dim7
Am7
A♯dim7
pie. It - 'll near - ly be like a pic - ture print by
legato
G/B
B7
Em
A7
D
C/D
Cur - ri - er and Ives. These won - der - ful
D
C/D
D
C/D
D
C/D
D7
D.S. 𝄋 al Fine
things are the things we re - mem - ber all through our lives! Just hear those

LET IT SNOW! LET IT SNOW! LET IT SNOW!

C7
F
F/A
A♭dim7
does - n't show signs of stop - ping, and I brought some corn for
C7
D7
Gm
D+
D7
Gm
A♭dim7
pop - ping. The lights are turned way down low. Let it
f
C7
F
C
snow, let it snow, let it snow! When we fi - nal - ly kiss good -
mf
C♯dim7
Dm7
G7
C
night, how I'll hate go - ing out in the storm! But if

B+ B♭6 A7 D7 G7
you real - ly hold me tight, all the way home I'll be
C F/C C7 F C7 F
warm. The fi - re is slow - ly dy - ing, and, my
mf
F/A A♭dim7 C7 D7 Gm D+ D7
dear, we're still good - bye - ing. But as long as you love me
Gm A♭dim7 C7
1. F
2. F
so, let it snow, let it snow, let it snow! Oh, the snow!
f
sfz

SANTA CLAUS' PARTY

Words and Music by
EDDIE POLA and GEORGE WYLE

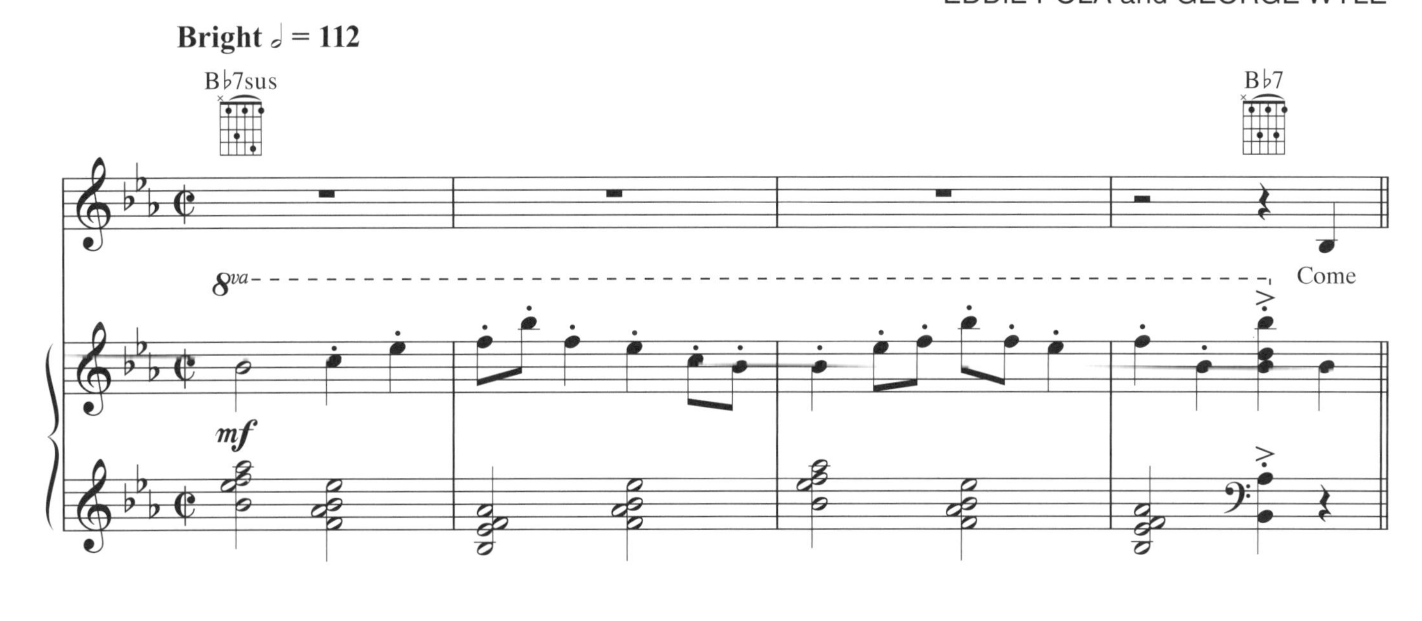

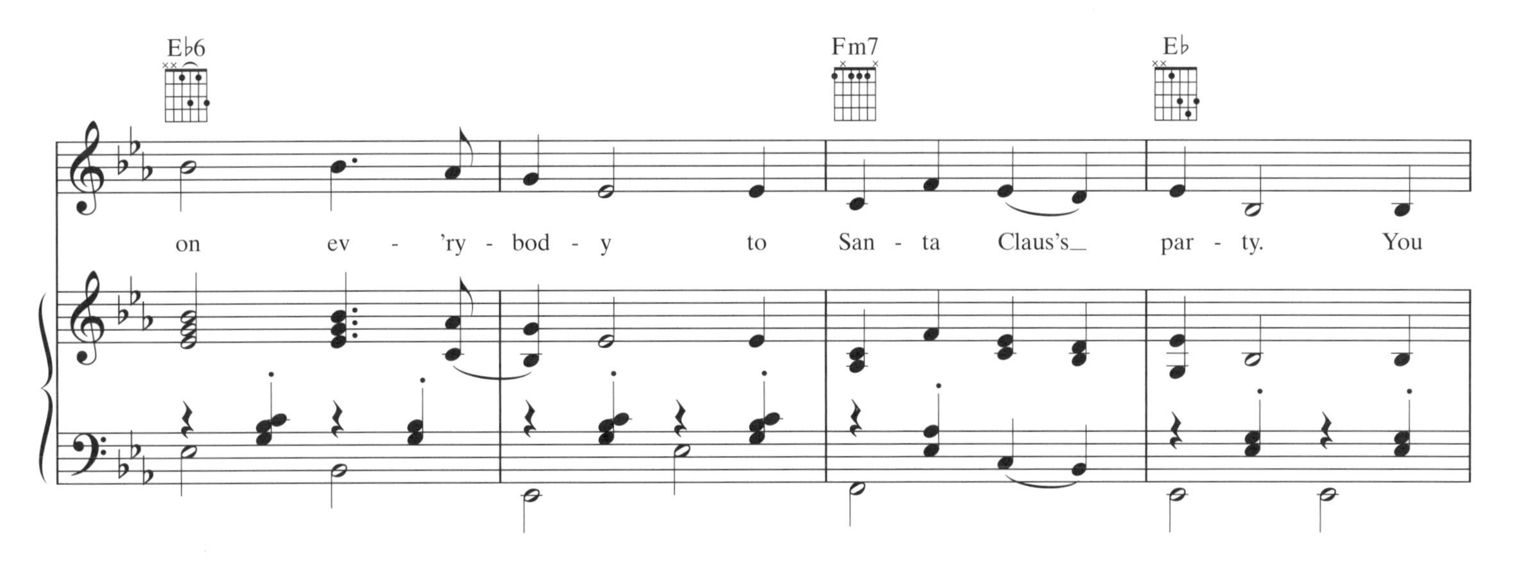

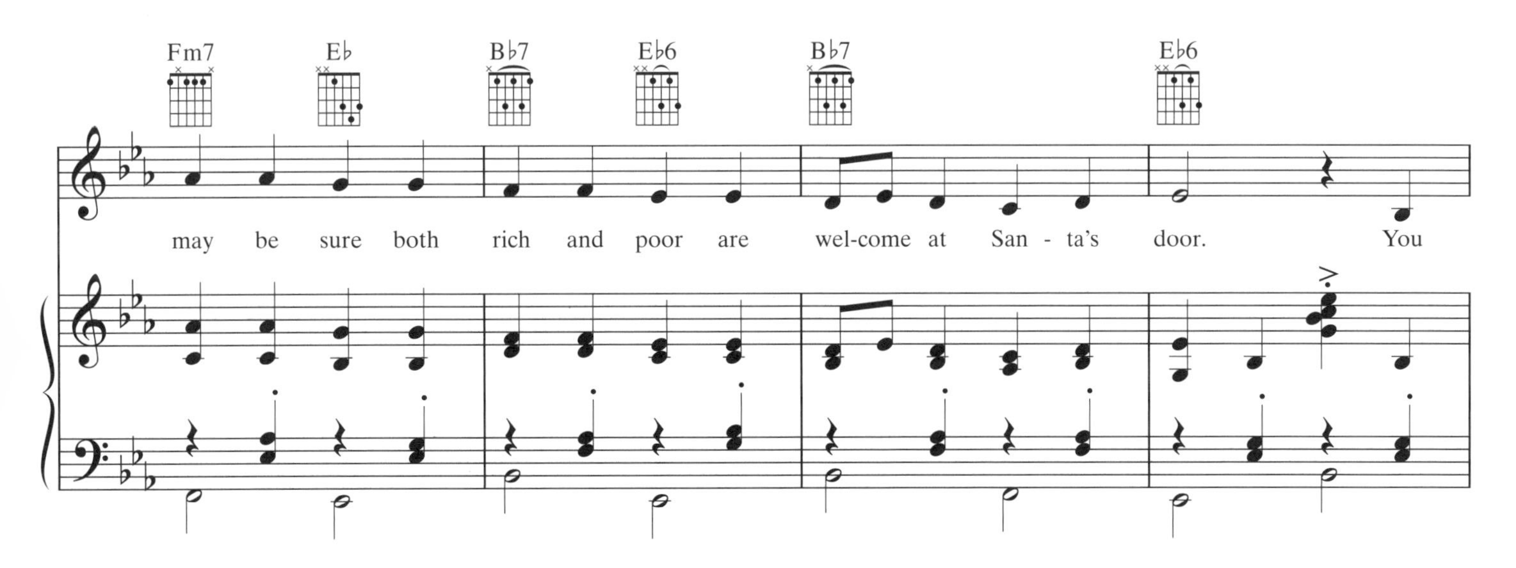

Fm7
E♭
don't need a tick - et to San - ta Claus's_ par - ty, a
Fm7
E♭
B♭7
E♭6
B♭7
E♭6
lot of toys for girls and boys and plen - ty of fun in store. A
B♭7
E♭7
A♭
B♭7
E♭7
A♭
Christ - mas tree so high, it pokes right through the sky. And
E♭6
B♭7
E♭6
Fm7
B♭7
San - ta will be there to call, "Mer - ry Christ - mas to you all!" Come

E♭6
Fm7
E♭
one ev - 'ry - bod - y to San - ta Claus's_ par - ty. A
Fm7
E♭
B♭7
E♭6
B♭7
E♭6
cheer - y grin will get you in, so what are you wait - ing for? There's a
A♭
E♭maj7
Fm7
B♭7
E♭6
base - ball bat for John - ny, a talk - ing doll for Jill. And a
Cm7
F7
B♭7
moun - tian high of ice cream pie where ev - 'ry - one eats his fill. There'll be
8va

Ab
Ebmaj7
Fm7
Bb7
Eb6
rides on San - ta's rein - deer with the Christ - mas - time pa - trol. If you're
Cm7
F7
Bb7
good they'll stop at San - ta's shop way up at the old North Pole! Come
Eb6
Bb7
Eb6
Fm7
Eb
on ev - 'ry - bod - y to San - ta Clause's par - ty. You
Fm7
Eb
Bb7
Eb6
Bb7
Eb6
may be sure both rich and poor are wel-come at San - ta's door. You

B♭7
E♭6
Fm7
E♭
don't need a tick - et to San - ta Claus's par - ty, a
Fm7
E♭
B♭7
E♭6
B♭7
E♭6
lot of toys for girls and boys and plen - ty of fun in store.
B♭/E♭
E♭6
Fm7
B♭7
E♭
A♭
Gm
Fm
E♭
B♭7
E♭

B♭/E♭
E♭6
Fm7
B♭7
E♭
A♭
Gm
Fm
E♭
B♭7
E♭
A
B♭7
E♭7
A♭
B♭7
E♭7
A♭
Christ - mas tree so high, it pokes right through the sky. And
E♭6
B♭7
E♭6
Fm7
B♭7
San - ta will be there to call, "Mer - ry Christ - mas to you all!" Come

E♭6
B♭7
E♭6
Fm7
E♭
one ev - 'ry - bod - y to San - ta Claus'__ par - ty. A
Fm7
E♭
B♭7
E♭6
B♭7
E♭
B♭7
E♭
cheer - y grin will get you in at
Fm7
B♭7sus
San - ta's Mer - ry Christ - mas
8va
E♭2
E♭
E♭6
par - ty!
(8va)

BABY, IT'S COLD OUTSIDE

Words and Music by
FRANK LOESSER

B♭6
Fm7
A♭/B♭
B♭7
so ver - y nice. My
so nice and warm. My
you'd drop in. I'll hold your hands, they're just like ice.
you dropped in. Look out the win - dow at that storm.
E♭
E♭maj7
E♭6
moth - er will start to wor - ry, and
sis - ter will be sus - pi - cious. My
Beau - ti - ful, what's your hur - ry?
Gosh, your lips look de - li - cious,
Edim7
fa - ther will be pac - ing the floor. So,
broth - er will be there at the door. My
Lis - ten to that fire - place roar.
waves up - on trop - i - cal shore.

B♭/F
Gm7
C7
real - ly I'd bet - ter scur - ry. Well, may - be just a half a drink more.
maid - en aunt's mind is vi - cious. Well, may - be just a cig - a - rette more.
Beau - ti - ful, please don't hur - ry.
Oh, your lips look de - li cious.
F7
B♭
B♭maj7
B♭6
The neigh - bors might think... Say,
I've got to get home. Say,
Put some rec - ords on while I pour. Ba - by, it's bad out there.
Nev - er such a bliz - zard be - fore. Ba - by, you'll freeze out there.
Cm7
F7
Cm7
F7
B♭
B♭maj7
what's in this drink? I wish I knew how
lend me your coat. You've real - ly been grand,
No cabs to be had out there. Your eyes are like
it's up to your knees out there. I thrill when you

B♭6
Fm7
B♭7
B♭7(♯5)
to break the spell.
I
but don't you see
there's
star-light now.
I'll take your hat,
your hair looks swell.
touch my hair.
How can you do
this thing to me?
E♭maj7
C9
ought to say, "No, no, no sir."
At least I'm gon-na say that I tried.
bound to be talk to-mor-row.
At least there will be plen-ty im-plied.
Mind if I move in clos-er?
Think of my life long sor-row
F7
B♭
B♭maj7
A♭7
G7
I real-ly can't stay.
Ah, but it's
I real-ly can't stay.
Ah, but it's
What's the sense of hurt-ing my pride.
Ba-by, don't hold out.
Ah, but it's
if you caught pneu-mo-nia and died.
Get rid of that hold out.
Ah, but it's

1.
C9
F7
B♭
Gm7
Cm7
F7
B♭
Gm7
cold out - side.
cold out - side.
8va
Cm7
F13
2.
C9
F13
2. I cold out - side.
cold out - side.
B♭
Gm7
Cm7
F7
B♭
Gm7
Cm9
F13
B♭6
3

JINGLE BELLS

Words and Music by
JAMES PIERPONT

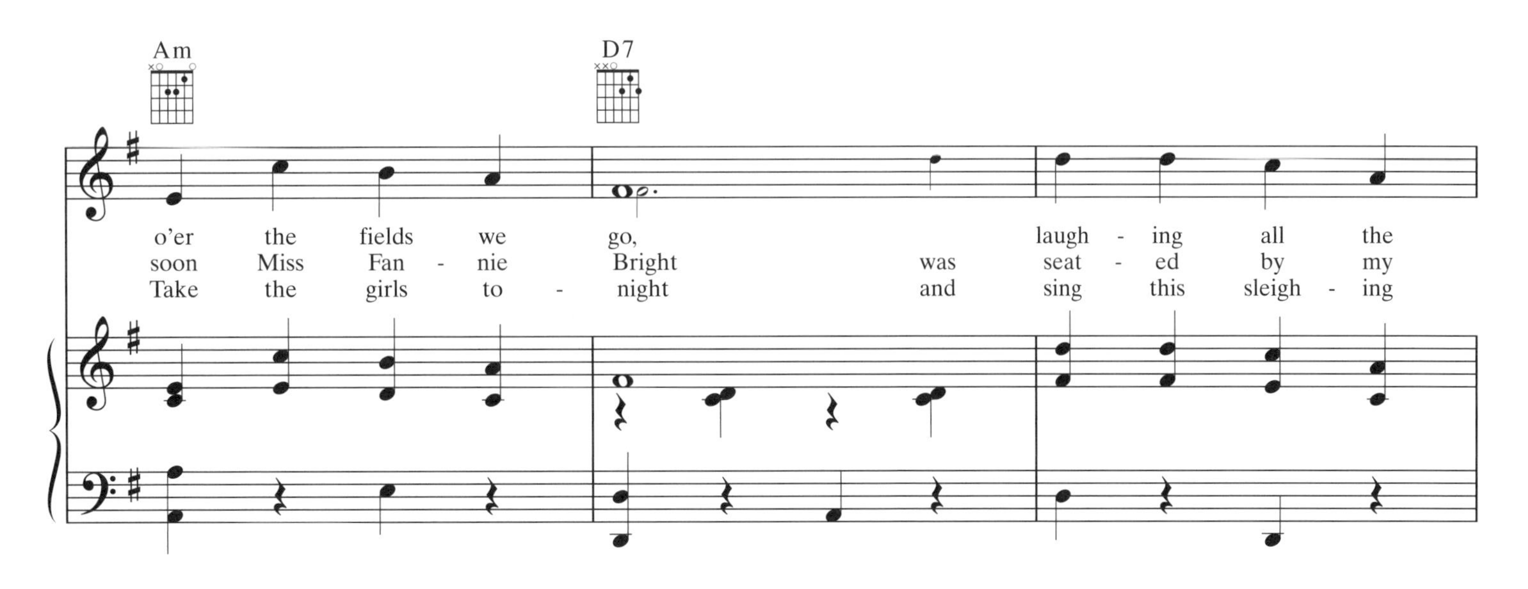

G
C
Am
G/D
D7
G
D7
way. Bells on bob - tail ring mak - ing spir - its bright; what fun it is to ride and sing a sleigh - ing song to - night.
side. The horse was lean and lank; mis - for - tune seemed his lot. He got in - to a drift - ed bank and whew, we got up - set!
song. Just get a bob - tailed nag, two - for - ty for his speed, then hitch him to an o - pen sleigh and crack, you'll take the lead!
Oh!
Chorus:
G
Jin - gle bells, jin - gle bells, jin - gle all the

C
G
way.
Oh, what fun it is to ride in a
A7
D7
G
one - horse o - pen sleigh!
Jin - gle bells,
C
jin - gle bells, jin - gle all the way.
Oh, what fun it
1.2.
3.
G
D7
G
G
is to ride in a one - horse o - pen sleigh! 2. A sleigh!

THE NUTCRACKER SUITE ("MARCH")

Composed by
PETER ILYICH TCHAIKOVSKY
Arranged by
BRIAN SETZER

Bright swing ♩ = 152

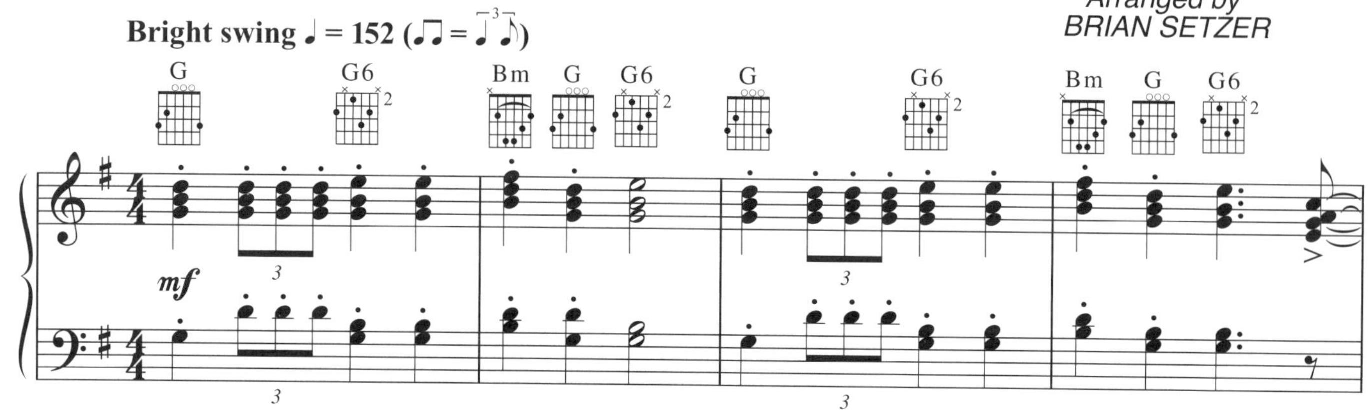

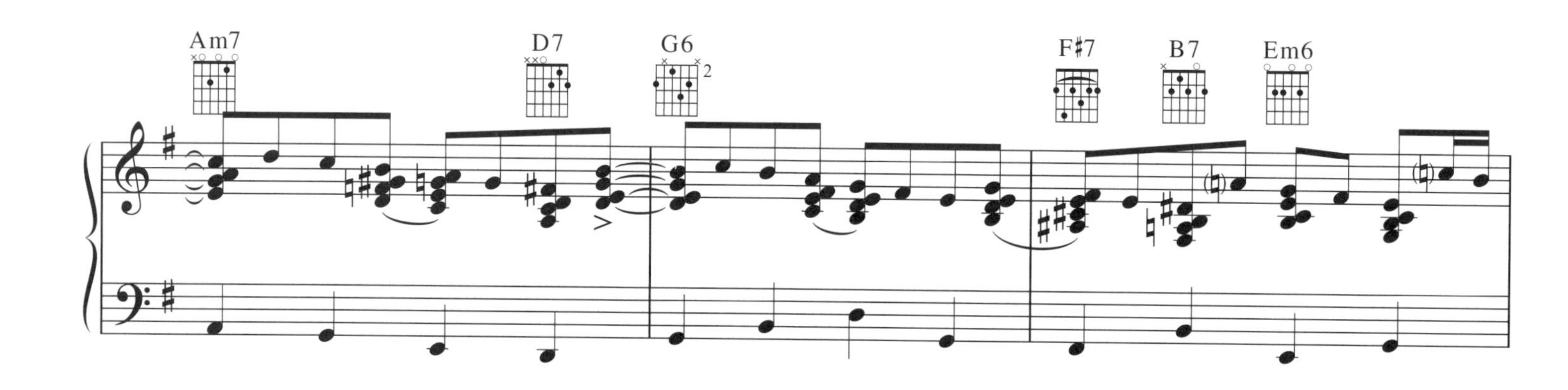

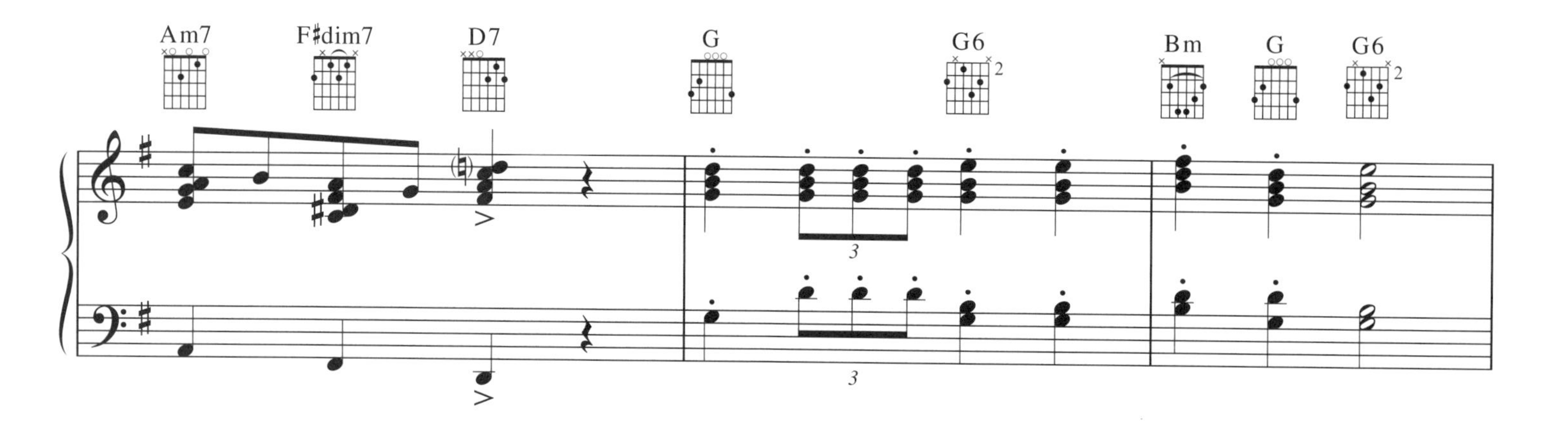

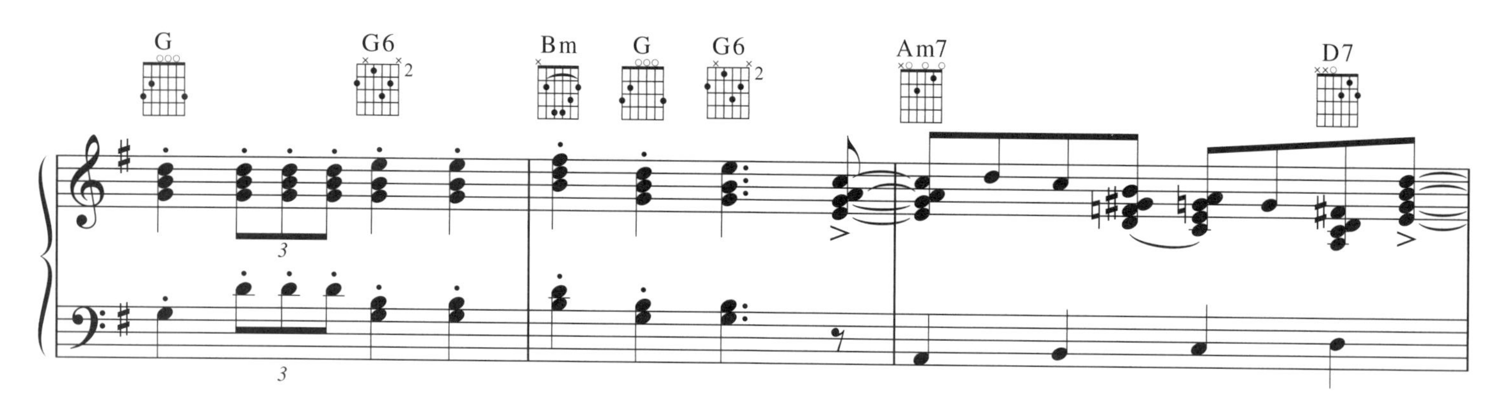

G6
Am7
Bm7
C6
B7
B
Em
Am7
F♯m7(♭5)
B
Em6
F♯m7(♭5)
B7
B
Em
Am7
F♯m7(♭5)
B
Em6
F♯7
B7
G
Em
Bm
G
Em
G
Em
Bm
G
Em
Am7
D7
G6
Am7
Bm7
Am7
D7
G6
Straight 8ths

CHRISTMAS ISLAND

Words and Music by
LYLE MORAINE

Moderate Island swing 𝅗𝅥 = 66

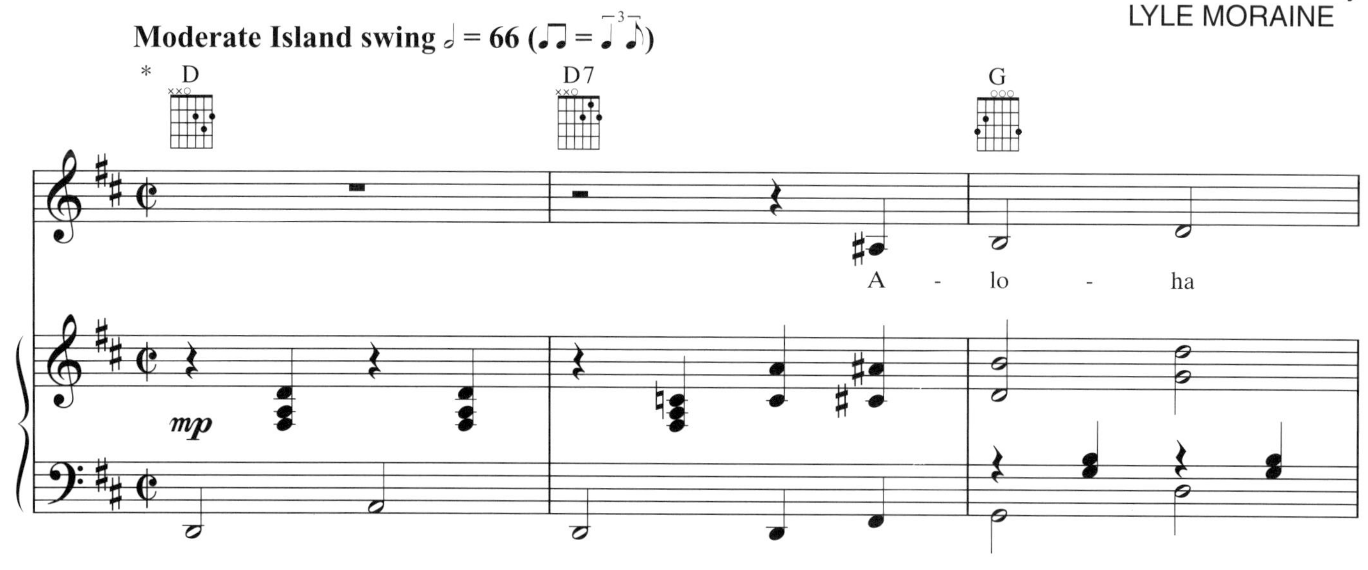

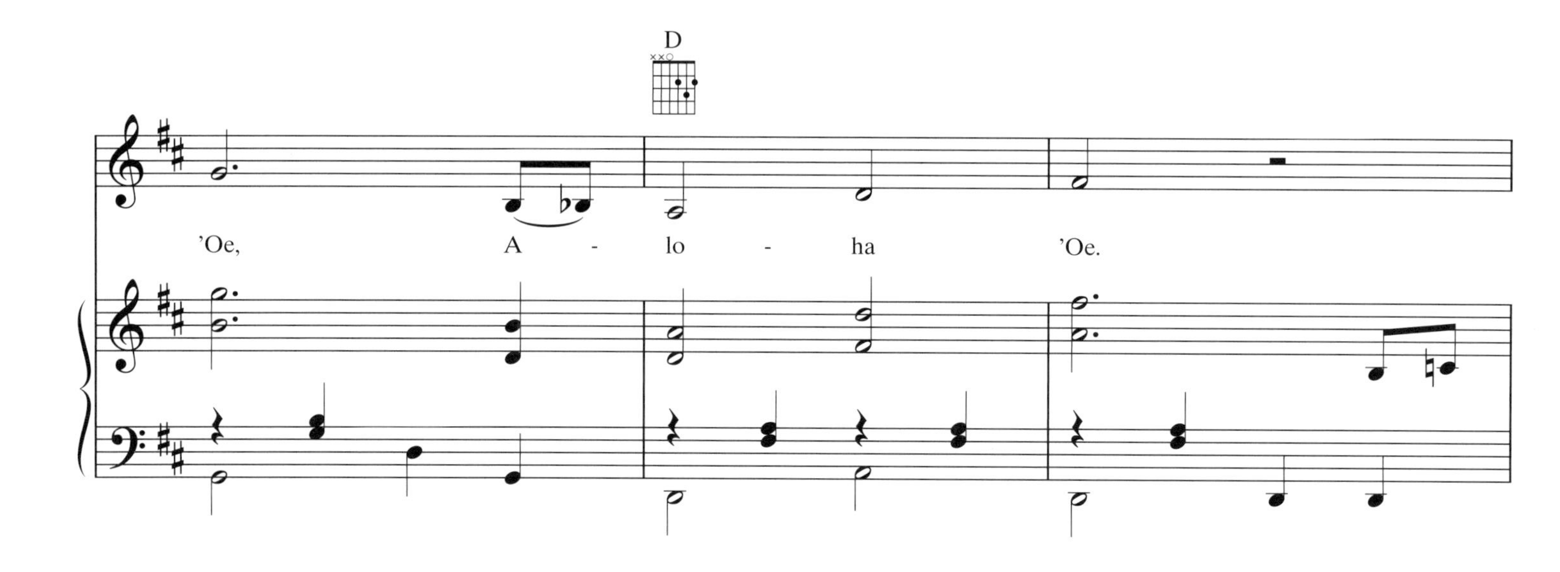

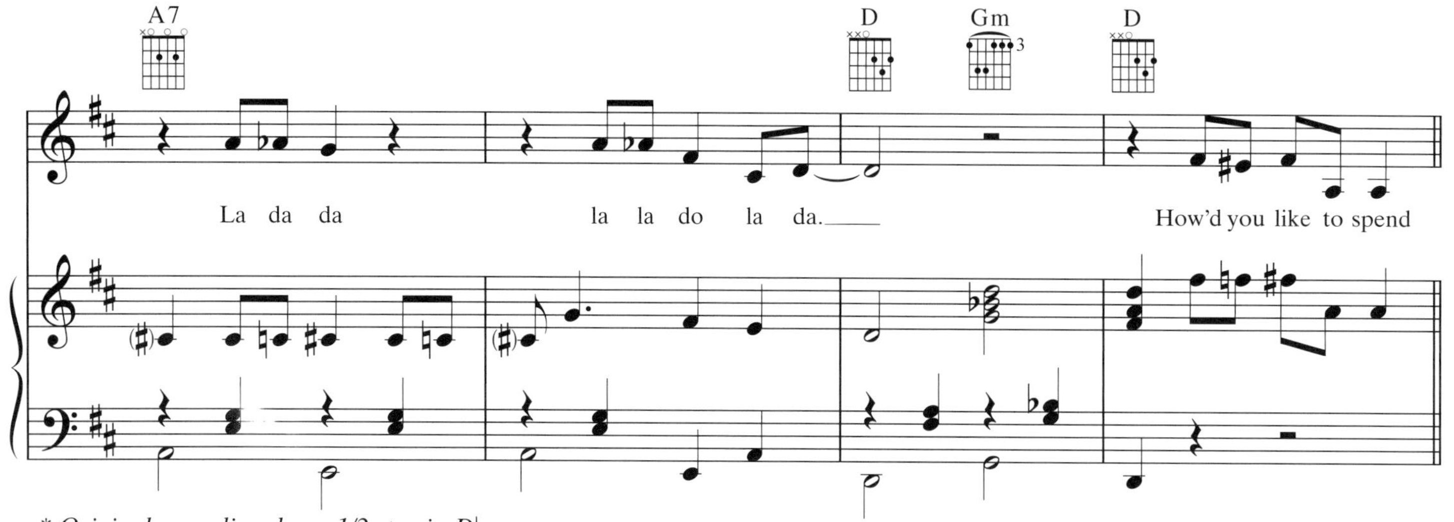

* *Original recording down 1/2 step in D♭.*

Verse:
G
B7
E7
Christ - mas on Christ - mas Is - land? How'd you
A7
D
D♯dim7
like to spend the hol - i - day a - way a - cross the sea?
A7
G
B7
How'd you like to spend Christ - mas on Christ - mas
E7
A7
Is - land? How'd you like to hang a stock-ing on a great big co - co - nut

D
D7
G
tree?
How'd you like to stay up late
Gm
D
B7
like the is - land - ers do,
wait for San - ta to
E7
A7
A♭7
A7
sail in with your pres - ents in a ca - noe?
If you ev - er spend
G
B7
E7
Christ - mas on Christ - mas Is - land,
you will

1.2.
3.
A7
D
D♯dim7
D7
G
Gm
never stray for ev-'ry day your Christ-mas dreams come true.
How'd you like to spend true.
A-lo-ha ha
'Oe.

SANTA BABY

Words and Music by
JOAN JAVITS, PHILIP SPRINGER
and TONY SPRINGER

A7 D7 G Em A7 D7
slip a sa - ble un - der the tree for me. Been an aw - ful good girl,
lit - tle thing I real - ly do need; the deed to a plat - i - num mine,
G Em Am D7 G Em
San - ta Ba - by, so hur - ry down the chim - ney to - night.
San - ta hon - ey, so hur - ry down the chim - ney to - night.
Am7 D7 G Em A7 D7
San - ta Ba - by, a 'fif - ty - four con - vert - i - ble, too,
San - ta cut - ie, and fill my stock - ing with a du - plex
3 3
G Em A7 D7 G Em
light blue. I'll wait up for you, dear San - ta Ba - by, so
and cheques. Sign your X on the line, San - ta cut - ie, and

Am D7 G Em Am7 D7 G
hur - ry down the chim - ney to - night.
hur - ry down the chim - ney to - night.
3 3
B7 F♯m7/B B7 E7 Bm7
Think of all the fun I've missed.
Come and trim my Christ - mas tree
Think of all the fel - las that I
with some dec - o - ra - tions bought at
E7 A7 A9sus A7
have - n't kissed.
Tif - fa - ny.
Next year I could be just as good if
I real - ly do be - lieve in you. Let's
3
D Am7/D D7 G Em
you check off my Christ - mas list.
see if you be - lieve in me.
San - ta Ba - by, I
San - ta Ba - by, for -
3 3

A7
D7
G
Em
want a yacht and real - ly that's not a - lot.
got to men - tion one lit - tle thing, a ring!
A7
D7
G
Em
Been an an - gel all year, San - ta Ba - by, so
I don't mean on the phone, San - ta Ba - by, so
Am
D7
1.
G
Em
hur - ry down the chim - ney to - night.
hur - ry down the chim - ney to - night.
Am7
D7
2.
G
Em
Am7
D7(♭9)
G6/9

SANTA CLAUS IS COMIN' TO TOWN

Words by
HAVEN GILLESPIE

Music by
J. FRED COOTS

G7 C Cm/E♭ G/D D7 G Gdim7 G7
I stopped off at the North Pole to spend a hol - i - day; I
He's got mil - lions of stock - ings to fill on Christ - mas Day; you'd
C G7 C G7 C C/E E♭dim7
called on dear old San - ta Claus to see what I could see. He
bet - ter write your let - ter now and mail it right a - way, be -
G/D B♭dim7 Am7 D7 G G7(♯5)
took me to his work - shop and told his plans to me.
cause he's get - ting read - y, his rein - deers and his sleigh.
So, you
Delicately
Refrain:
C C7 F/C Fm/C C C7 F Fm
bet - ter watch out, you bet - ter not cry. Bet - ter not pout, I'm tell - ing you why:
mf

C Am F6 G7 C Am7 G7
San - ta Claus is com - in' to town. He's
C C7 F/C Fm/C C C7 F Fm
mak - ing a list and check - ing it twice, gon - na find out who's naugh - ty and nice.
C Am F6 G7 C Cdim7
San - ta Claus is com - in' to town. He
mf
C7 F C7 F
sees you when you're sleep - in'. He knows when you're a - wake. He

D7 G G♯dim7 Am7 D7 G G7(♯5)
knows if you've been bad or good so be good for good - ness sake. Oh, you
p
C C7 F/C Fm/C C C7 F Fm
bet - ter watch out, you bet - ter not cry. Bet - ter not pout, I'm tell - ing you why:
C Am F6 G7 C G7
San - ta Claus is com - in' to town. With
C F C F Fm
lit - tle tin horns and lit - tle toy drums, root - y toot - toots and rum - my tum - tums,
mp

C
G7
C
G7
San - ta Claus is com - in' to town.
And
8va
C
F
C
F
Fm
cur - ly - head dolls that tod - dle and coo,
el - e - phants, boats, and kid - die cars too;
loco
C
G7
C
Cdim7
San - ta Claus is com - in' to town.
The
8va
loco
mf
C7
F
C7
F
kids in girl and boy - land will have a ju - bi - lee.
They're

D7
G
G♯dim7
Am7
D7
gon - na build a toy - land town all a - round the Christ - mas
G
G7(♯5)
C
F
tree. So, you bet - ter watch out, you bet - ter not cry.
mp
C
F
Fm
C
Bet - ter not pout, I'm tell - ing you why: San - ta Claus is
8va
G7
C
com - in' to town.
(8va)
3

NOTHING FROM NOTHING

Words and Music by
BILLY PRESTON and BRUCE FISHER

Bright rag tempo 𝅗𝅥 = 104

Verse:
C6
B7
E7
Am7
1.4. Noth ing from noth - ing leaves noth - ing.
2. I'm not trying to be your he - ro,
3. Noth - ing from noth - ing leaves noth - ing
sim.
Gm7
C7
F
E7
You got - ta have some - thing if you wan-na be with me.
'cause that ze - ro is too cold for me.
and I'm not stuff - ing, be - lieve you me.
Dm7
G7
Am
Gm7
C9
F
Noth - ing from noth - ing leaves noth - ing.
I'm not trying to be your high - ness,
Don't you re - mem - ber, I told you,
E7
A7
D7
G7
C7
You got - ta have some - thing if you wan-na be with me, yeah.
'cause that mi - nus is too low to see, yeah.
I'm a sol - dier in the war on pov - er - ty, yeah.

To Coda
1.2.
3.
Instrumental:
C6
B7
E7
Am7
Gm7
C7
F
E7
Dm7
G7
Am7
Gm7
C7
F

E7
A7
D7
G7
C7
D.S. 𝄋 al Coda
𝄌 Coda
C7
Repeat ad lib. and fade

WINTER WONDERLAND

Words by
DICK SMITH

Music by
FELIX BERNARD

E♭
Fm7/B♭
E♭maj7
B♭7
E♭
Cm
heav - en of dia - monds shine down thru the night; two hearts are thrill - in' in
F7
B♭7
E♭maj7
Cm7
E7
B♭7
spite of the chill in the weath - er.
E♭
Fm7/B♭
E♭
Fm7/B♭
E♭
Fm7/B♭
Love knows no sea - son, love knows no clime, ro - mance can blos - som
E♭maj7
B♭7
E♭
Cm
F7
B♭7
an - y old time. Here in the o - pen, we're walk - in' and hop - in' to -

Refrain:
E♭maj7
Cm
E7
B♭7
E♭
geth - er!
Sleigh - bells ring, are you
p–f
B♭7
lis - t'nin'? In the lane, snow is glis - t'nin'. A
F7
B♭7
beau - ti - ful sight, we're hap - py to - night, walk - in' in a win - ter won - der -
E♭
land! Gone a - way is the blue - bird, here to

B♭7
stay is a new bird.
He sings a love song
He's sing - ing a song
as
F7
B♭7
E♭
we go a - long,
walk - in' in a win - ter won - der - land!
G
D7
G
D7
In the mead - ow, we can build a snow - man,
then pre - tend that he is Par - son
and pre - tend that he's a cir - cus
G
B♭
F7
B♭
Brown.
clown.
He'll say, "Are you mar - ried?" We'll say, "No, man! But
We'll have lots of fun with Mis - ter Snow - man, un -

C7
F7
B♭7
E♭
you can do the job when you're in town!" Lat - er on, we'll con -
til the oth - er kid - dies knock 'em down! When it snows, ain't it
B♭7
spire, as we dream by the fire, to
thrill - in', though your nose gets a chill - in'? We'll
F7
B♭7
face un - a - fraid the plans that we made, walk - in' in a win - ter won - der -
frol - ic and play the Es - ki - mo way, walk - in' in a win - ter won - der -
1.
E♭
B♭7
2.
E♭
land! Sleigh - bells land!